MORE *Viz* CRAP JOKES

WIFE &
3 KIDS
TO
SUPPORT

A HALF-ARSED COMPENDIUM FEATURING
THE PICK FROM 10 YEARS' WORTH
OF TRULY UNREMARKABLE JOKES

**Written and drawn at Pinewood Studios, England, and on location in Newcastle
upon Tyne, Scotland. Additional contributions from Jim Blz, Roger Radio,
John Fardell, Steve Olive and Mrs. R. G. Stayrt.**

INTRODUCTION
by Dr Jonathan Miller

What is a joke? At a very basic level, I suppose it is some-
thing which tends to make us laugh. But what is laughter?
Joseph Addison, who I just looked up in a dictionary of
quotations, would have us believe it is the "faculty which
distinguishes man from all other beasts" (apart from hyenas).
He may have had a point. As everybody knows, all living
things have four senses: Touch, feel, sight, and smell.
Human beings, on the other hand, have a remarkable and
mysterious fifth sense - the sense of humour. It is this sense
which means that you - as a human being - will probably
appreciate this little book somewhat more than would,
say, a snail or an ocelot.

For my own part, when it comes to jokes,
I have always concurred with Schopenhauer
in his belief that there's nothing funnier than
the sudden apprehension of an incongruity
between a general concept and a heteroge-
neous object which is subsumed thereunder,
and hence between what is abstract and what is
perceptive. When that happens I piss myself.

4

The Crap Joke in Question.

Fig. 1
Light from the Sun is reflected off the joke, and enters the eye via the cornea. The zonular ligament deforms the lens to focus the joke upon the retina, where light sensitive cells called rods and cones convert the joke into a pattern of nerve impulses.

Fig. 2
These electrical impulses pass down the optic nerve, through the parieto-occipital sulcus (a) and into the occipital lobe of

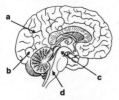

the brain (b). From here, they are transmitted to the mesencephalon (c), the area of the brain responsible for getting jokes. A signal is then sent along the medulla oblongata (d) and into the spinal cord, where it branches, activating neurons in both the central and peripheral nervous systems.

Fig. 3
The impulses in the central system trigger involuntary contractions of the zygomaticus major and levator labii superioris muscles, coupled with an explosive exhalation through the larynx - what doctors call laughing.

Fig. 5
In this instance, the joke in question is so funny, that the electrical impulses in the peripheral nervous system have exceeded 0.0006 milliamps, causing relaxation of the internal urethral sphincter muscle (a) leading to inadvertent intra-trouseral micturition.

Fig.4
At the same time, the impulses in the peripheral system cause a regular and synchronised contraction and relaxation of the biceps brachii and triceps brachii muscles in the upper arm. The effect of this is a repeated percussive slapping of the hand on the vastus lateralis muscle of the upper leg.

Note. Should any of the above physiological responses fail to take place whilst you are reading this book, the most likely reason is that there is a tumour, possibly the size of a grapefruit, growing in the middle of your brain. Consult a doctor who may recommend experimental surgery, leaving your head looking like an old-fashioned leather football. In mild cases it may merely be necessary to undergo a course of electro-convulsive therapy causing you to jerk around on a table, pop-eyed, whilst biting a stick.

6

7

9

10

11

12

13

14

16

19

21

22

23

24

26

CRAB'S JOKE

CAN YOU TELL ME HOW TO GET TO THE TESTICLES?
SORRY. I'M A STRANGER ROUND THESE PARTS MYSELF.

30

32

JOYRIDING/JUMPER JOKE

36

STEVE OLIVE

40

42

43

44

49

53

54

55

Tailor Shop Joke

63

68

69

70

71

73

74

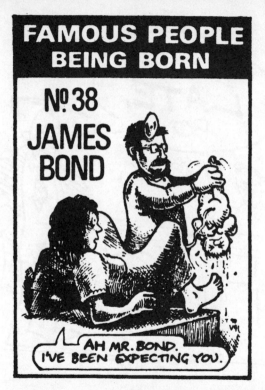

81

82

87

INDEX

COUNCIL LITTER COLLECTION DEPOT.

I DON'T KNOW IF I CAN DO THIS JOB.

DON'T WORRY. YOU'LL PICK IT UP AS YOU GO ALONG.